THE ANT'S PANIC

Quran Stories for Little Hearts

SANIYASNAIN KHAN

Designed and Illustrated by
Achla Anand & Achal K. Anand

Goodword Books Pvt. Ltd.
1, Nizamuddin West Market
New Delhi-110 013
Tel. 435 6666, 435 5454, 435 1128
Fax 9111-435 7333, 435 7980
e-mail: info@goodwordbooks.com

Goodwordkidz

Helping you build a family of faith

First published 2002
© Goodword Books 2002

The Prophet Sulayman ﷺ was the son of the Prophet Dawud ﷺ. He was a mighty king and ruled Jerusalem. He was given wonderful powers by Allah. As a child, Sulayman ﷺ showed wisdom and intelligence. At a very young age he surprised his father with his ideas about the rule of law.

It was when two angry men came to see Dawud ﷺ. One of them said, "I had a beautiful field full of crops. This man's sheep entered it and destroyed all my plants."

Dawud said that the owner of the field was in the right and that he should take the sheep to make up for his loss. But Sulayman 🕊, who was a boy at that time, gave a better solution to the problem. "I would like to suggest," said Sulayman 🕊 "that the sheep be given to the owner of the field, who will use their milk and wool."

"After a while when the crops are fully grown, the sheep will be returned to their owner." In this way Sulayman  showed the difference between what was owned and what could be earned from it.

When Sulayman ﷺ grew up, he was blessed with Prophethood and became the king too. Allah gave him special knowledge.

He was able to
understand the language
of the birds.

By Allah's special favour he could control the winds.

14

He was also in control of the jinn.
He used to employ them in any
way he liked.

One day Sulayman ﷺ was
passing through a valley
along with his mighty army.
In the valley there lived a
large number of ants.

18

Seeing the huge army coming, one of the ants at once shouted a warning to its fellow ants: "Get into your homes before Sulayman and his army tread on you by mistake!"

Sulayman عليه السلام heard what the ant said and smiled. Because of Allah's great boon to him, he was able to understand languages that others could not.

He was suddenly startled by the realization of how merciful Allah had been to him. He turned to his Lord in praise and prayed: "O my Lord! Make me grateful to You for Your favours, which You have given me and my parents, and inspire me to do what is right to please You. And through Your grace, admit me among Your righteous servants." (*Surah an Naml* 27:19)

Find Out More

To know more about the message and meaning of Allah's words, look up the following parts of the Quran which tell the story of the Prophet Sulayman ﷺ:

Surah an-Naml 27:15-19

ﷺ *Alayhis Salam* 'May peace be upon him.'
The customary blessings on the prophets.